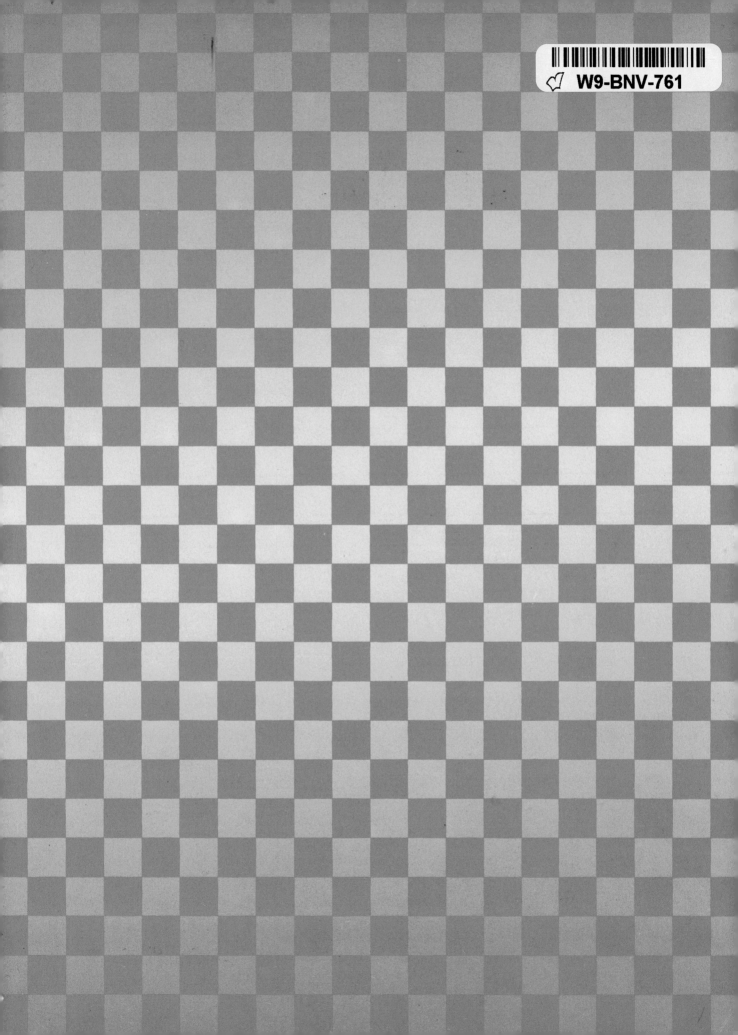

AUTHORS

ELAINE MEI AOKI

VIRGINIA A. ARNOLD

JAMES FLOOD

JAMES V. HOFFMAN

DIANE LAPP

MIRIAM MARTINEZ

ANNEMARIE SULLIVAN

  PALINCSAR

MICHAEL PRIESTLEY

NANCY ROSER

CARL B. SMITH

WILLIAM H. TEALE

JOSEFINA VILLAMIL

  TINAJERO

ARNOLD W. WEBB

PEGGY E. WILLIAMS

KAREN D. WOOD

MACMILLAN/McGRAW-HILL SCHOOL PUBLISHING COMPANY

NEW YORK   CHICAGO   COLUMBUS

AUTHORS, CONSULTANTS, AND REVIEWERS

WRITE IDEA! Authors

Elaine Mei Aoki, James Flood, James V. Hoffman, Diane Lapp, Ana Huerta Macias, Miriam Martinez, Ann McCallum, Michael Priestley, Nancy Roser, Carl B. Smith, William Strong, William H. Teale, Charles Temple, Josefina Villamil Tinajero, Arnold W. Webb, Peggy E. Williams

The approach to writing in Macmillan/McGraw-Hill Reading/Language Arts is based on the strategies and approaches to composition and conventions of language in Macmillan/McGraw-Hill's writing-centered language arts program, WRITE IDEA!

Multicultural and Educational Consultants

Alma Flor Ada, Yvonne Beamer, Joyce Buckner, Helen Gillotte, Cheryl Hudson, Narcita Medina, Lorraine Monroe, James R. Murphy, Sylvia Peña, Joseph B. Rubin, Ramon Santiago, Cliff Trafzer, Hai Tran, Esther Lee Yao

Literature Consultants

Ashley Bryan, Joan I. Glazer, Paul Janeczko, Margaret H. Lippert

International Consultants

Edward B. Adams, Barbara Johnson, Raymond L. Marshall

Music and Audio Consultants

John Farrell, Marilyn C. Davidson, Vincent Lawrence, Sarah Pirtle, Susan R. Snyder, Rick and Deborah Witkowski

Teacher Reviewers

Terry Baker, Jane Bauer, James Bedi, Nora Bickel, Vernell Bowen, Donald Cason, Jean Chaney, Carolyn Clark, Alan Cox, Kathryn DesCarpentrie, Carol L. Ellis, Roberta Gale, Brenda Huffman, Erma Inscore, Sharon Kidwell, Elizabeth Love, Isabel Marcus, Elaine McCraney, Michelle Moraros, Earlene Parr, Dr. Richard Potts, Jeanette Pulliam, Michael Rubin, Henrietta Sakamaki, Kathleen Cultron Sanders, Belinda Snow, Dr. Jayne Steubing, Margaret Mary Sulentic, Barbara Tate, Seretta Vincent, Willard Waite, Barbara Wilson, Veronica York

ACKNOWLEDGMENTS

The publisher gratefully acknowledges permission to reprint the following copyrighted material:

"Bet You Can't" by Penny Dale. Copyright © 1987 by Penny Dale. First published in England by Walker Books Ltd. London. Reprinted by arrangement with HarperCollins Publishers.

"Everything Grows" with text by Raffi and photographs by Bruce McMillan. Text copyright © 1989 by Troubadour Learning, a division of Troubadour Records Ltd. Book photographs including front cover photograph copyright © 1989 by Bruce McMillan. Front cover Raffi photograph copyright © David Street. Back cover Raffi photograph copyright © Patrick Harbron. All rights reserved. No part of this book may be reproduced or transmitted in any form or by any means, electronic or mechanical, including photocopying, recording, or by any information storage and retrieval system, without permission in writing from the publisher. Published by Crown Publishers, Inc., 225 Park Avenue South, New York, New York 10003. CROWN is a trademark of Crown Publishers, Inc. RAFFI SONGS TO READ and SONGS TO READ are trademarks of Troubadour Learning, a division of Troubadour Records Ltd. Used by permission of Troubadour Learning, a division of Troubadour Records Ltd.

"Grown Up Chairs" by Nicholas Palmer and Michelle O'Brien-Palmer with art by Kevin Jonson from THROUGH MY EYES by Nicholas Palmer and Michelle O'Brien-Palmer. Reprinted by permission of MicNik Publications and Kevin Jonson. Copyright © 1990 by Nicholas Palmer and Michelle O'Brien-Palmer, P.O. Box 3041, Kirkland, WA 98083.

"Send Us a Rainbow" in NOOTKA AND QUILEUTE MUSIC by Frances Densmore from Bureau of American Ethnology Bulletin 124, page 285, Washington, D.C. United States Printing Office, 1939. Used by permission of Smithsonian Institution Press.

"The End" from NOW WE ARE SIX by A. A. Milne. Copyright 1927 by E.P. Dutton, renewed © 1955 by A. A. Milne. Used by permission of Dutton Children's Books, a division of Penguin Books USA Inc.

"Tommy" from BRONZEVILLE BOYS AND GIRLS by Gwendolyn Brooks. Copyright © 1956 by Gwendolyn Brooks Blakely. Reprinted by permission of HarperCollins Publishers.

"Whose Baby?" by Masayuki Yabuuchi. Copyright © 1981 by Masayuki Yabuuchi. Reprinted by permission of Philomel Books and Fukuinkan Shoten Publishers.

"You'll Soon Grow into Them, Titch" by Pat Hutchins. Copyright © 1983 by Pat Hutchins. Reprinted by permission of Greenwillow Books, a division of William Morrow and Company, Inc., Publishers, New York.

COVER DESIGN: WYD Design
COVER ILLUSTRATION: Jean Hirashima
DESIGN CREDITS
Sheldon Cotler + Associates Editorial Group
Designframe Incorporated, 74-75

ILLUSTRATION CREDITS
José Ortega, 6-9; Judith Sutton, 42-43; Seymour Chwast, 74-75; Janelle Hagen, 132.

PHOTOGRAPHY CREDITS
All photographs are by the Macmillan/McGraw-Hill School Division (MMSD) except as noted below.
40: Mario Ruiz/Picture Group. 41: Courtesy of Bruce McMillan. 71: Andy Sherwill. 76: Courtesy of Masayuki Yabuuchi. 102: Bo Jarner. 103: t.l. Grant Heilman; m.r. Bo Jarner. 131: Courtesy of Pat Hutchins.

1995 Printing

Macmillan/McGraw-Hill School Division
10 Union Square East
New York, New York 10003

Printed in the United States of America
ISBN 0-02-178752-2 / 1, L.2
   7 8 9 RRW 99 98 97 96 95

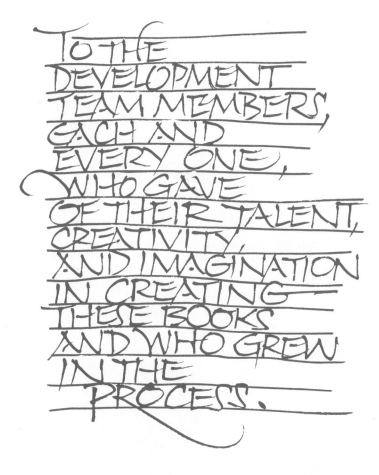

To the Development Team members, each and every one, who gave of their talent, creativity, and imagination in creating these books and who grew in the process.

Samuel Gesumaria
Linda Kucan

HeRe we Grow!

CONTENTS

In summer the rains come,
The grass grows up,
and the deer has new horns.

A YAQUI POEM

EVERYTHING GROWS

Written by

Raffi

Photographed by

Bruce McMillan

Everything grows and grows.

Babies do,

animals too.
Everything grows.

Everything grows and grows.
Sisters do,

brothers too.
Everything grows.

A blade of grass,

fingers and toes,

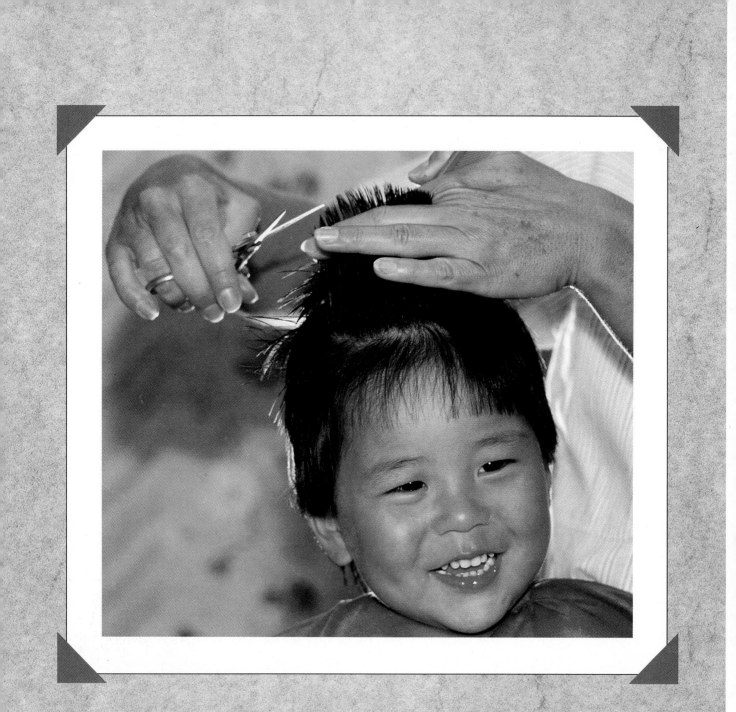

hair on my head,

a red, red rose.
Everything grows, anyone knows,
that's how it goes.

Everything grows and grows.
Babies do,

animals too.
Everything grows.

Everything grows and grows.

Sisters do, brothers too.
Everything grows.

Food on the farm,

fish in the sea,

birds in the air,

leaves on the tree.

Everything grows, anyone knows,

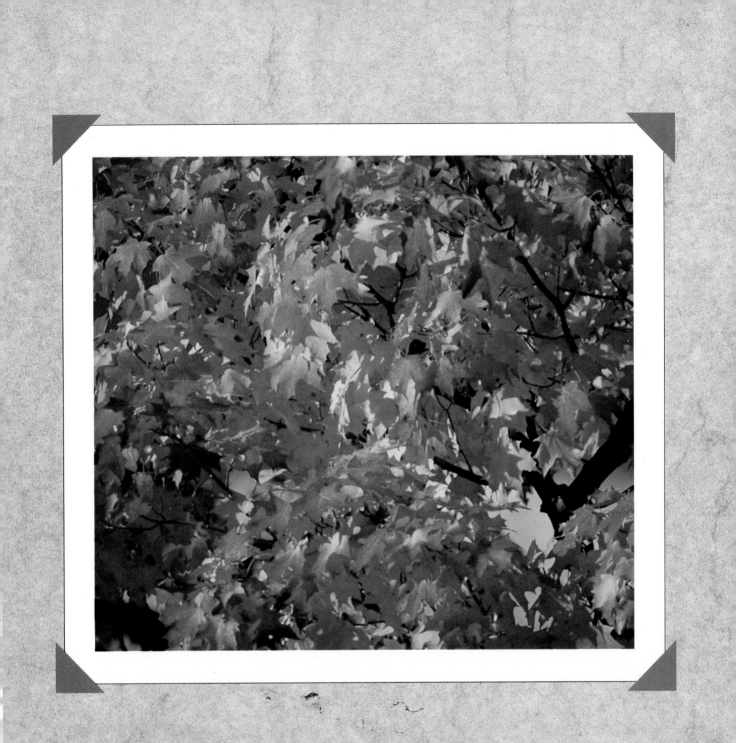

that's how it goes.

That's how it goes, under the sun.

That's how it goes, under the rain.
Everything grows, anyone knows,
that's how it goes.

Yes, everything grows and grows.
Babies do,

animals too.
Everything grows.

Everything grows and grows.

Sisters do, brothers too.
Everything grows.

Mamas do,

papas too.

Everything grows.

MEET RAFFI

Raffi got the idea for *Everything Grows* when he was in an airplane that was landing. "All around the airport was a forest," he says. "And suddenly, when I saw all those trees, I thought *things grow!* It made me want to write a song about the wonderful magic of growing life, and about how people are part of this magic."

Now Raffi is singing songs for people of all ages. These songs are about how important it is to take care of the earth so all living things can keep growing.

MEET BRUCE McMILLAN

Bruce McMillan likes his pictures to tell little stories of their own. In *Everything Grows,* he wanted the brother and sister to look like they were playing a game about growing taller.

He also likes his pictures to be funny. "Did you notice that this book has the three little pigs in it?" he asks. "It's my own little joke."

Mr. McMillan asks children he meets to be models in his pictures. He tells them, "You never know when you might be in one of my books!"

Tommy

I put a seed into the ground
And said, "I'll watch it grow."
I watered it and cared for it
As well as I could know.

One day I walked in my back yard,
And oh, what did I see!
My seed had popped itself right out,
Without consulting me.

Gwendolyn Brooks

43

BET. YOU CAN'T

by Penny Dale

45

48

49

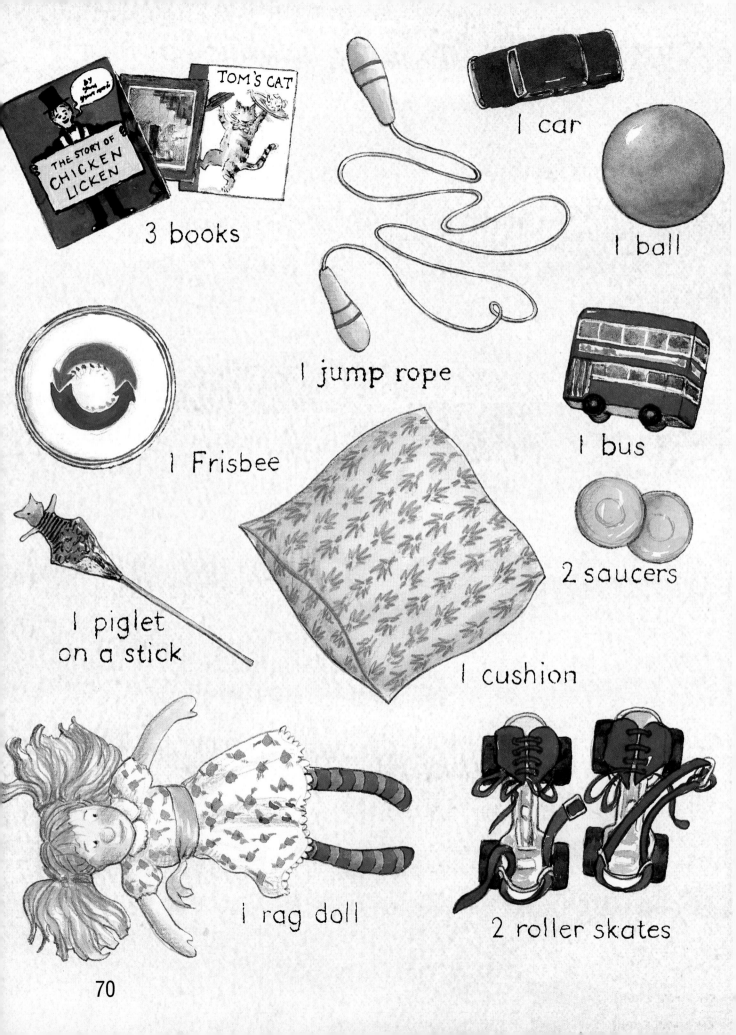

3 books

1 jump rope

1 car

1 ball

1 Frisbee

1 jump rope

1 bus

2 saucers

1 piglet on a stick

1 cushion

1 rag doll

2 roller skates

Meet Penny Dale

Penny Dale's little girl gave her the idea for *Bet You Can't*. When her daughter was three years old, she didn't like to do what Ms. Dale asked. So Penny Dale told her, "Bet you can't." The game worked. The little girl showed her that she could do whatever her mother wanted.

She tells children, "You can make a game of doing something boring. When someone doesn't want to do a job that needs to be done, try saying, 'Bet you can't,' and see what they do."

Grown Up Chairs

Have you ever noticed that
Most seats aren't made for you?
If kids made all the chairs around
We'd have chairs that fit us too.

Some restaurant chairs are very low.
Some chairs are very high.
So your chin is on the table
Or your head is in the sky.

Movie seats are really funny,
They fold your legs into your face.
Your mom has to pull you out
If you don't sit in the right place.

Sometimes there's no chair at all
So I get squished with mom or dad.
Sometimes heads get in the way,
So I can't see and I feel sad.

We can sit up on our knees
And they're OK you know.
It helps us fit in grown up chairs
Until our bodies grow.

Kindergartener Nicholas Palmer
and his mother,
Michelle O'Brien-Palmer

Leo the Late Bloomer

by Robert Kraus

illustrated by José Aruego

Simon and Schuster, 1987

Spring Is Here

by Taro Gomi

illustrated by Taro Gomi,
Chronicle, 1989

Meet Masayuki Yabuuchi

Masayuki Yabuuchi says, "Ever since I was little, I have loved birds and other animals. I never get tired of watching them. Most of all, I love to watch animal families. So I thought it would be nice to make a picture book about them, like *Whose Baby?*

"When I watch how animals live and move, I get lots of ideas for books," the artist says. "I want to show children what animals really look like."

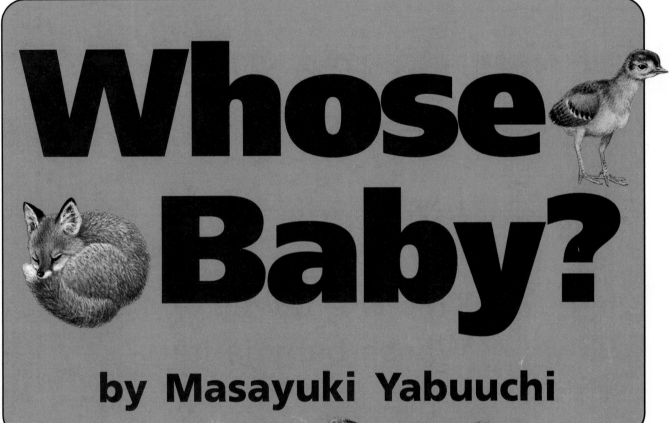

Whose Baby?

by Masayuki Yabuuchi

This is a fawn.
Whose baby is it?

A fawn is a baby deer.

It belongs to a father and mother deer, called a buck and a doe.

It belongs to a peacock
and peahen.

This cub is curled up fast asleep.
Whose baby is it?

It is a fox cub.

It belongs to a fox and
a vixen.

This cub is wide awake—
whose cub is it?

It belongs to a lion and lioness.

It belongs to a bull seal
and a cow seal.

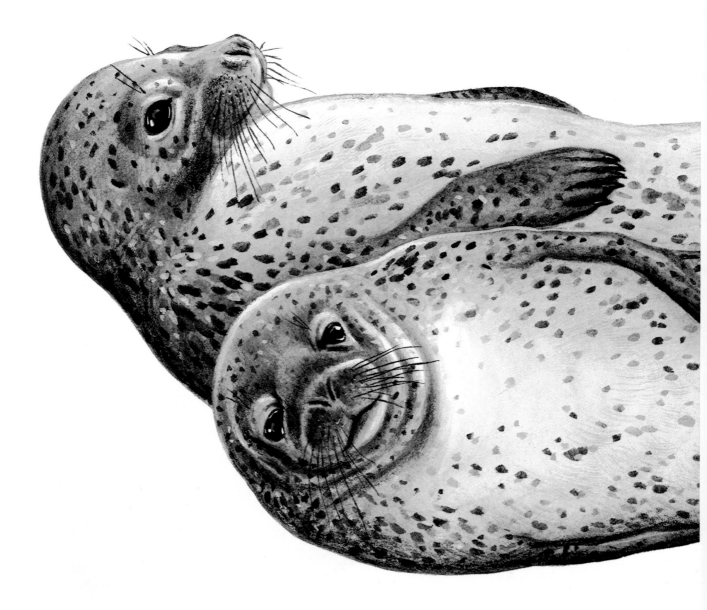

This is a calf.
Whose baby is it?

It is a baby bison.
It belongs to a bull bison
and cow bison.

A

BABY

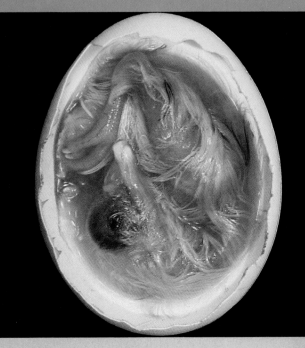

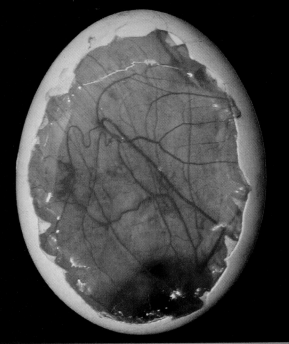

A baby chick is growing inside this egg. The chick needs food and air to live and grow. The chick's food comes from the yolk of the egg. Air comes into the egg through tiny holes in the shell.

CHICK

After twenty-one days, the chick is ready to hatch out of the egg. It makes a tiny hole in the shell and keeps tapping until the shell breaks open.

Then the chick comes out of the shell.

103

You'll Soon Grow into Them, Titch by Pat Hutchins

Titch needed new pants.

His brother Pete said,
"You can have my old pants,
they're too small for me."

"They're still a bit big for me,"
said Titch.

"You'll soon grow into them,"
said Pete.

And when Titch needed a new sweater,

110

his sister Mary said,
"You can have my old sweater,
it's too small for me."

"It's still a bit big for me,"
said Titch.

"You'll soon grow into it,"
said Mary.

And when Titch needed new socks,

they both said,
"You can have our old socks,
they're too small for us."

115

"And I'll soon grow into them,"
said Titch.

"I think," said Mother, "that Titch should have some new clothes."

So Dad and Titch went shopping.

118

They bought a brand-new pair of pants,

a brand-new sweater,

and a brand-new pair of socks.

And when Mother brought
their brand-new baby home,
Titch wore the new clothes.

"There," said Titch,
"he can have my old pants,

124

and my old sweater,

and my old socks.
They're much too small for me!"

"They're a bit big for him,"
said Pete and Mary.

"He'll soon grow into them,"
said Titch.

Meet
Pat Hutchins

Pat Hutchins says, "I wrote *You'll Soon Grow into Them, Titch* for my son Sam. He has an older brother, Morgan. When Morgan grew out of his clothes, he gave them to Sam. Suddenly, we realized that Sam never had any new clothes of his own. So we went out and bought him his own new set of clothes."

About the pictures, Ms. Hutchins tells children, "The story is all about growing, so I put a bird's nest in the pictures. When Mother's baby is born, the baby birds have hatched."

Janelle Hagen

The End

When I was One,
I had just begun.

When I was Two,
I was nearly new.

When I was Three,
I was hardly Me.

When I was Four,
I was not much more.

When I was Five,
I was just alive.

But now I am Six, I'm as clever as clever.
So I think I'll be six now for ever and ever.

A. A. Milne